AWESOME *Women* ACTIVITY BOOK

ARCTURUS

ARCTURUS

This edition published in 2020 by Arcturus Publishing Limited
26/27 Bickels Yard, 151–153 Bermondsey Street, London SW1 3HA

Authors: Julia Adams and Lisa Regan
Illustrator: Louise Wright
Art Direction: Jessica Holliland
Designer: Elaine Wilkinson
Editor: Donna Gregory
Editorial Manager: Joe Harris

ISBN: 978-1-78950-815-4
CH007557NT
Supplier 42, Date 1219, Print run 9004

Printed in Singapore

CONTENTS

STAND UP AND SHOUT OUT!

There are 7.7 billion people living on Earth, and just over half of them are women. And yet women are under-represented in so many ways. Many girls are not allowed to attend school, nor choose who they marry, nor take part in politics. Only a small proportion of top jobs are held by women, and there are far fewer female surgeons, firefighters, chefs, pilots, and computer scientists than their male counterparts. Something needs to change!

WOMEN IN SAUDI ARABIA WERE ONLY ALLOWED TO VOTE FOR THE FIRST TIME IN 2015, AND TO DRIVE IN 2018.

And things *are* changing in many parts of the world. Only 100 years ago, women in the US and the UK won the right to vote in elections. People began to talk about the rights of women to do all kinds of things that had been traditionally associated with men. In recent times, lots of women have chosen to move beyond the role of mother and housewife, and have entered the workplace to earn money.

Now, intelligent, talented women can ignore gender stereotypes and make their own way in life. Girls are bravely standing up for what they believe in, even if they live in countries where their views put their lives at risk. It can be a tough task. Successful women will tell you that you have to work harder, shout louder, and push yourself farther to be noticed in a crowd of males. But they will also tell you to go for it.

You might have to overcome obstacles along the way, but that will make you tougher and smarter. Don't just limit yourself to one ambition—pick a few things you want to do, and reach for the stars!

INTERNATIONAL WOMEN'S DAY IS CELEBRATED GLOBALLY ON MARCH 8, AND HIGHLIGHTS THE SOCIAL, ECONOMIC, CULTURAL, AND POLITICAL ACHIEVEMENTS OF WOMEN.

IN JUNE 2019, ONLY 33 OF THE TOP 500 US BUSINESSES WERE RUN BY WOMEN, BUT IN 2000, IT WAS ONLY TWO! HOW MANY WILL IT BE IN 2030?

IN GENERAL, GIRLS' BRAINS MATURE TWO YEARS EARLIER THAN BOYS' BRAINS.

IN 2019, AROUND 65 MILLION GIRLS STILL DID NOT GO TO SCHOOL.

SO, WHAT DO YOU WANT TO DO? YOU LIVE IN A WORLD WHERE OTHER WOMEN HAVE MADE IT POSSIBLE TO BE WHATEVER YOU WANT TO BE. IT'S UP TO YOU TO CHOOSE YOUR PATH IN LIFE.

BLOG LIKE MALALA

MALALA YOUSAFZAI
Education activist

Born: 1997 in Pakistan

Famous for: Blogging for the BBC about life under the Taliban

Life changers: She was shot after speaking out about Pakistani girls being banned from school. She addressed the UN on her sixteenth birthday, demanding that all children have the right to an education.

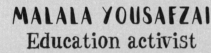

YOU CAN DO IT!
Start your own blog

Malala was 11 when she began writing her blog. She recorded her feelings about the fighting going on around her, and her daily life attending school before it was closed down. She wrote about her friendships, her fears, and even the dreams she had at night.

Malala hand-made notes and then passed them to a reporter to post them online. Write your own blog notes here. What is it going to be about? What message do you want to spread? Choose something you're interested in, such as the environment, cookery, sports, or making fun things out of waste. Keep safe by never revealing any details (like your school name, or your address) that could identify you or your friends. Have fun making up codenames instead!

"We realize the importance of our voices only when they are silenced."

Malala Yousafzai received the Nobel Peace Prize when she was just 17, making her the youngest ever winner of the award.

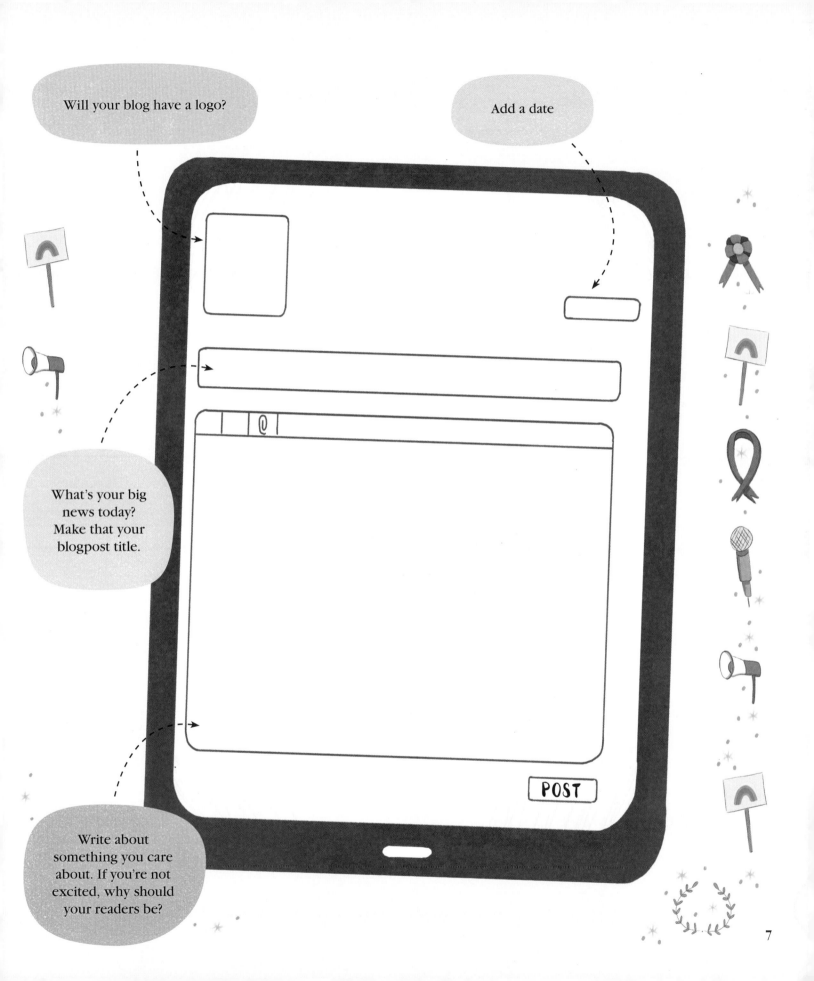

CAMPAIGN LIKE EMMELINE

EMMELINE PANKHURST
Women's rights activist

Lived: 1858-1928 in the UK and Canada

Famous for: Campaigning for votes for women

Life changers: Founded the Women's Franchise League (1889) and the Women's Social and Political Union (1903) with the motto "Deeds Not Words." She became known for using strong tactics to draw attention to her cause, including hunger strikes.

BALLOT BOX

VOTES FOR WOMEN

"We are here not because we are lawbreakers; we are here in our efforts to become lawmakers."

YOU CAN DO IT!
Make your voice heard

Emmeline Pankhurst and her supporters became known as suffragettes. (Their name came from the word "suffrage," which is the right to vote.) They took their campaign around Britain and overseas, spreading the message that women everywhere should be allowed to vote. What do you believe in?

Design a logo to go on this T-shirt. Make it eye-catching and bright so everyone will want to spread your message!

Do you feel strongly about animal rights, or the environment? Think of some catchy or powerful slogans and write them on the placards.

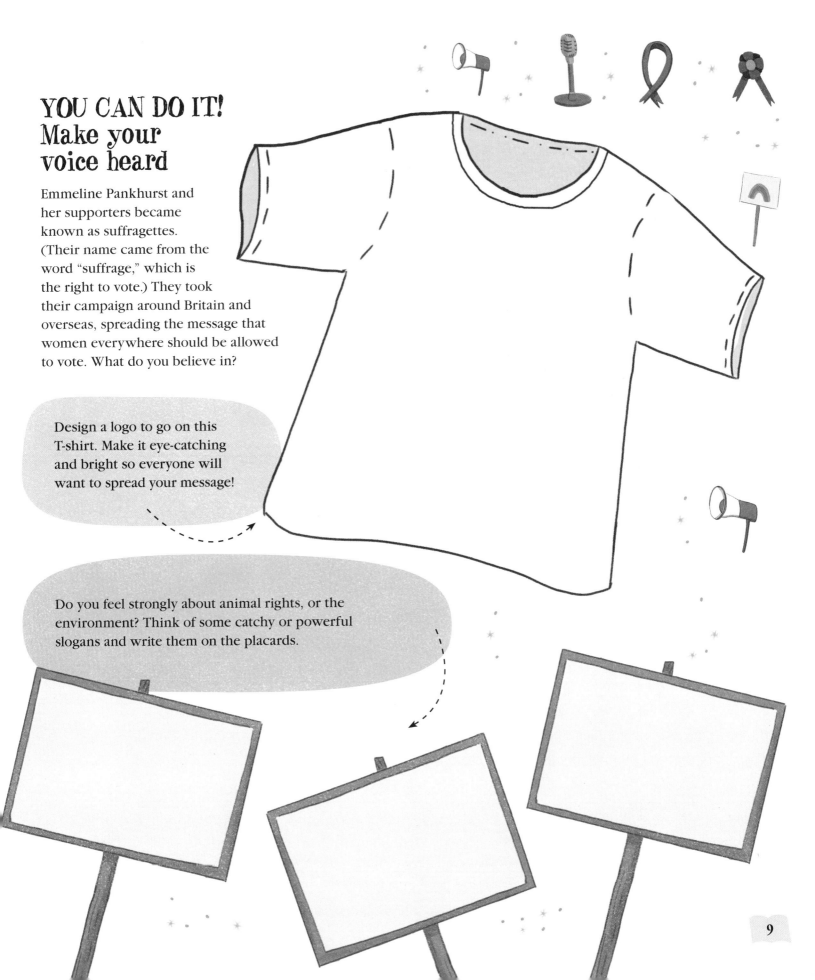

LEARN TO SPEAK LIKE HELEN

HELEN KELLER
Activist and author

Lived: 1880–1968 in the US

Famous for: Overcoming deafness and blindness to gain her college degree

Life changers: An illness when she was a small child destroyed her sight and hearing. Aged six, she found a tutor who helped her learn to read and speak. As an adult, she became a world-famous speaker and author.

"Although the world is full of suffering, it is full also of the overcoming of it."

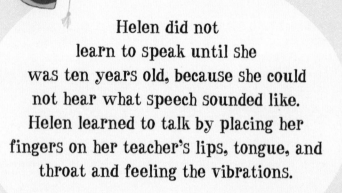

Helen did not learn to speak until she was ten years old, because she could not hear what speech sounded like. Helen learned to talk by placing her fingers on her teacher's lips, tongue, and throat and feeling the vibrations.

YOU CAN DO IT!
Learn how to fingerspell

Helen's tutor, Anne Sullivan, was partially blind herself. One of the ways they communicated was by spelling words into the other person's open hand. These are the symbols they used. Can you learn to spell your name, and form a greeting?

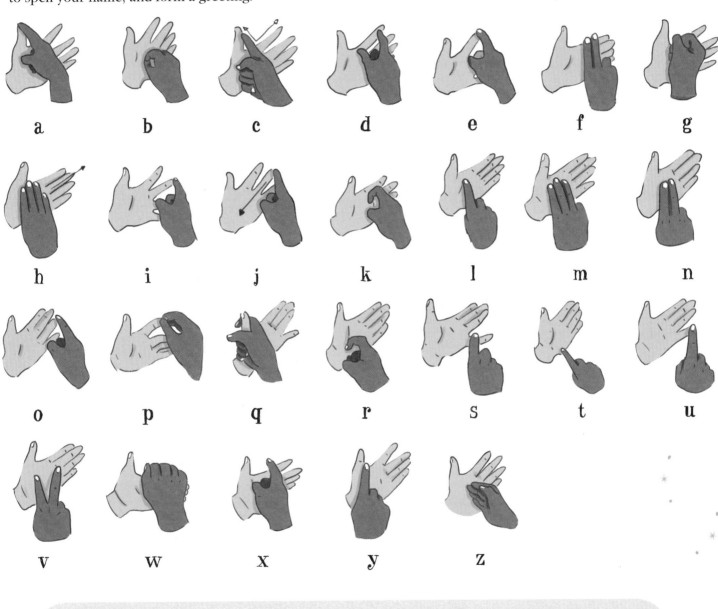

For example, "Helen" would be:

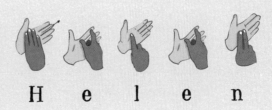

H e l e n

BLAST-OFF LIKE VALENTINA

VALENTINA TERESHKOVA
Cosmonaut
(Soviet astronaut)

Born: 1937 near Moscow, Russia

Famous for: Being the first (and youngest) woman to fly in space

Life changers: Studied part-time while working in a factory as a teenager; applied to Soviet space program in 1961; chosen for the Vostok 6 mission launched in June 1963.

YOU CAN DO IT!
See the world from space

Valentina had a special view of the Earth from space that was very rare at the time. These days, we are lucky enough to have technology that allows us all to gaze at our planet and see its wonders. We can use Google Earth to view landforms from space—the "Airplane boneyard" is one such fascinating sight.

1. You will need access to Google Earth. It is completely free (and safe) to download and use. Just type it into a search engine and follow the instructions, but make sure your parent or guardian knows you're doing this.

2. Type the name of a place into the search box on the left-hand side of the screen. Start with your home address to see what it looks like from space.

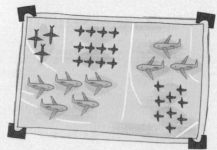

3. Now use the Search tool to find the Airplane boneyard. As you type, various options will appear. Choose the one in Tucson, Arizona. Wow, huh?!

These planes are no longer in use, but are stored in the Arizona desert where the dry climate prevents them rusting so their parts can be reused if needed. It is quite a sight, looking down on more than 4,000 old aircraft! What else will you look for? How about herds of buffalo in Tanzania, the Star Fort in the Netherlands, or the North Pole in the Arctic Circle?

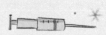

YOU CAN DO IT!
See the ISS in orbit

Space exploration has changed since the 1960s when Tereshkova undertook her mission. The US and Russia no longer compete in the "space race" but work together with many other countries on the International Space Station (ISS) which has been orbiting Earth since 1998. On a clear night, you might be able to see it passing overhead!

The ISS looks like a bright star moving across the sky, from horizon to horizon. You will be lucky if you see it by chance, but you can look online to find out when it will be flying above your part of the world. Use the Heaven's-Above website, NASA's "Spot the Station," or one of the special phone apps to track its position.

Google Sky lets you explore space using images from the Hubble Telescope and NASA satellites.

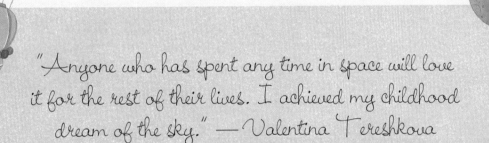

"Anyone who has spent any time in space will love it for the rest of their lives. I achieved my childhood dream of the sky." — Valentina Tereshkova

ISS is the largest human-made item orbiting the Earth at that height, and the third brightest object in the night sky. It has been visited by people from at least 18 countries and has room for six crew to live onboard.

BE AMAZING LIKE GRACE

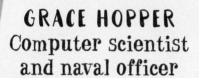

GRACE HOPPER
Computer scientist
and naval officer

Lived: 1906–1992 in the US

Famous for: Writing a breakthrough computer coding language

Life changers: Part of a top-secret naval project at Harvard University in 1943; worked on the world's first commercial electronic computer (UNIVAC I) in 1949; reached rank of rear admiral and finally retired a few months before her eightieth birthday.

"It is often easier to ask for forgiveness than to ask for permission."

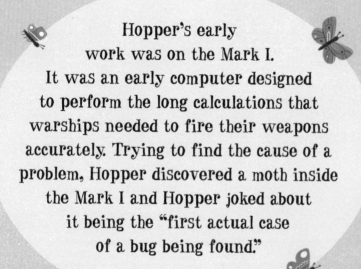

Hopper's early work was on the Mark I. It was an early computer designed to perform the long calculations that warships needed to fire their weapons accurately. Trying to find the cause of a problem, Hopper discovered a moth inside the Mark I and Hopper joked about it being the "first actual case of a bug being found."

YOU CAN DO IT! Program a friend

Try inventing your own programming language and write a simple program to make a friend perform an activity, such as going to another room and getting a glass of water. Each line of your code should give an instruction for a single short and very simple action. Ask them to not do anything unless the instructions specifically say to do it, and keep amending your instructions until your friend can complete the activity. Use the notepad for your first go, and then write your final instructions neatly on the tablet screen.

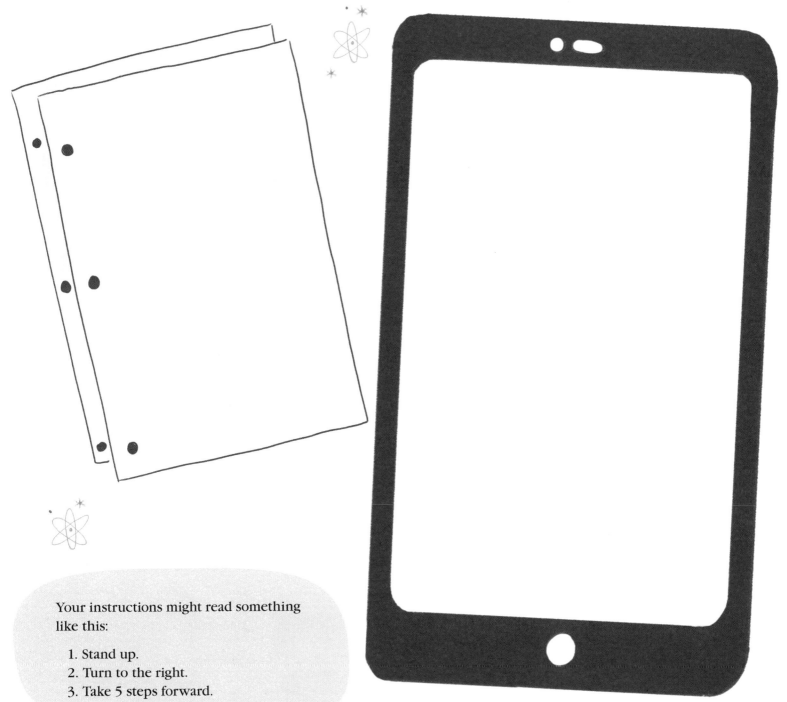

Your instructions might read something like this:

1. Stand up.
2. Turn to the right.
3. Take 5 steps forward.

GO GREEN LIKE WANGARI

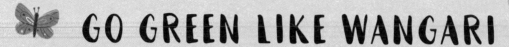

WANGARI MAATHAI

Lived: 1940–2011 in Kenya

Famous for: Her Green Belt Movement has planted over fifty million trees in Africa

Life changers: A professor at Nairobi University in 1977, the same year she started the Green Belt Movement, which paid women to plant trees. Since then tens of thousands of women have earned a living helping the environment.

Trees need bees and butterflies, but they are not the only creatures that pollinate plants. Ants, wasps, beetles, moths, birds, and even bats do the job as well.

"We cannot tire or give up. We owe it to the present and future generations of all species to rise up and walk!"

YOU CAN DO IT! Be a bee friend

Each one of Wangari's women contributed their own small effort to make a big difference to the natural world. Play your part, by making seed bombs to scatter. Once they have grown, they will attract important pollinators such as bees and butterflies.

1. Pour three cups of potting soil or compost into a large container. Add two cups of dry clay mix and one cup of water. If you can't get clay mix, use one cup of flour instead. Mix them well, adding a drop more water if you need to make them bind together.

2. You will need a packet of mixed wildflower seeds. Sprinkle a few on to your soil, and knead them in. Don't add too many as they need room to grow.

3. If you like, add a sprinkle of paprika. This will stop any birds from eating your seeds (but won't harm them).

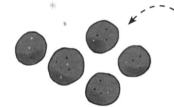

4. Pinch off enough mix to roll into a ball about the size of a large marble. Make lots, and store them overnight in a box so they can dry out.

5. Check the weather forecast. The best time to throw your seed bomb is the day before rain is due. Don't worry, though, if it doesn't rain for a few days.

BE SURE TO USE FLOWERS THAT ARE INDIGENOUS TO YOUR AREA. DON'T THROW SEED BOMBS ONTO PRIVATE PROPERTY OR MANAGED CONSERVATION AREAS.

BOUNCE BACK LIKE VENUS & SERENA

VENUS WILLIAMS
Tennis player

Born: 1980 in California, US

Famous for: Trailblazing diversity in sport

Life changers: Venus reached the final of the US Open in 1997 as the first ever unseeded player. She won four Olympic gold medals between 2000 and 2016.

SERENA WILLIAMS
Tennis player

Born: 1981 in Michigan, US

Famous for: Dominating women's tennis with extraordinary skill, power, and athleticism

Life changers: Serena won a Career Golden Slam (Olympic gold plus all four Grand Slam tournaments) in singles and TWO in doubles with her sister Venus.

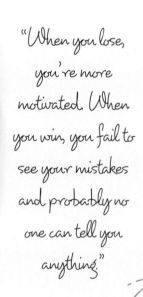

"When you lose, you're more motivated. When you win, you fail to see your mistakes and probably no one can tell you anything"

YOU CAN DO IT!
Snatch victory from defeat

The Williams sisters trained together from a young age; their parents saw tennis as a path out of poverty, and did everything they could to push them along the path to success. The girls gave each other support and healthy competition. Both of them have admitted to making mistakes, sometimes very publicly, but learning from them. If things don't go to plan, there are still valuable lessons to be learned.

What's the most embarrassing mistake you have made? What did you learn from it?

Speak to your relatives and ask them about their mistakes, or their embarrassing moments. What lessons did those mistakes teach them? What would you have learned from them? Write an account of the funniest, or the most instructive, here.

DREAM BIG LIKE J. K. ROWLING

JOANNE (J. K.) ROWLING
Writer, film producer, and philanthropist

Born: 1965 near Bristol, England

Famous for: Inventing a whole new world inhabited by the young wizard Harry Potter

Life changers: Her first book was rejected several times before being published in 1997; now the Harry Potter series has been translated into 65 languages, turned into movies, made her extremely wealthy, and earned her an OBE award from the Queen of the United Kingdom.

YOU CAN DO IT!
Use your imagination (and dream BIG things)

J. K. Rowling is the world's most successful author. She is a master at weaving magic through her books, not only into her characters but through the plotlines, settings, and incredible, fantastical beasts.

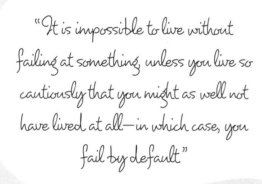

"It is impossible to live without failing at something, unless you live so cautiously that you might as well not have lived at all—in which case, you fail by default"

Let your mind roam free and make up names and characteristics for each of these creations.

1. What species is it?

....

2. What is this one called?

....

3. Is it good or evil (or a bit of both)?

....

4. Does it have special powers?

....

5. What does it sound like?

....

6. Where can you find it?

....

1. What species is it?

....

2. What is this one called?

....

3. Is it good or evil (or a bit of both)?

....

4. Does it have special powers?

....

5. What does it sound like?

....

6. Where can you find it?

....

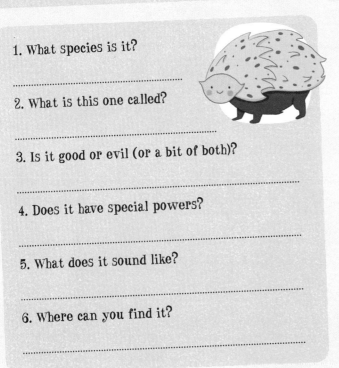

1. What species is it?

....

2. What is this one called?

....

3. Is it good or evil (or a bit of both)?

....

4. Does it have special powers?

....

5. What does it sound like?

....

6. Where can you find it?

....

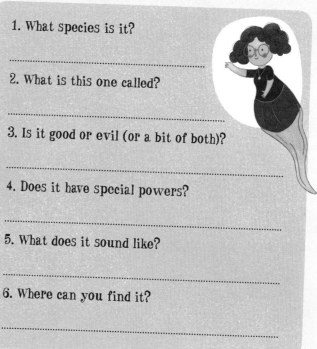

1. What species is it?

....

2. What is this one called?

....

3. Is it good or evil (or a bit of both)?

....

4. Does it have special powers?

....

5. What does it sound like?

....

6. Where can you find it?

....

GET SKILLS LIKE MARTA

MARTA
Soccer player

Born: 1986 in Alagoas, Brazil

Famous for: Being at the very top of the game of women's soccer; simply the best

Life changers: Told at age 5 that soccer was not for girls, she refused to listen, and trained with the boys. She was talent-spotted at 14, and was voted FIFA Women's World Player of the Year six times, between 2006 and 2018.

YOU CAN DO IT!
Practice makes perfect

Like many soccer players, Marta's skills on the pitch are the result of years and years of practice. Her control of the ball is exemplary, she runs past players as if they aren't there, and she finishes with confidence. That's how, during the 2019 World Cup, she became the first player (female or male) to score at five different FIFA World Cup tournaments.

"There may be tough times, but the difficulties which you face will make you more determined to achieve your objectives and to win against all the odds."

BACK OF THE NET!

Here's a little trick you can teach yourself. It's called "Around the world."

First, learn how to balance the ball on top of your dominant foot without letting it roll off. Try to keep it there for as long as possible.

Now bounce it up and down (juggle it) on that foot. Aim for it to go straight up and down, with no spin or sideways movement. Keep it low; don't juggle it too hard or too high.

When you're confident, juggle the ball up and loop your foot a full 360 degrees around the ball while it is in midair. You can go in either direction, whichever feels easiest.

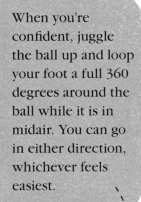

THE AIM IS TO COMPLETE THE LOOP BEFORE THE BALL TOUCHES THE GROUND, SO YOU CAN CATCH THE BALL ONCE MORE ON THE TOP OF YOUR BOOT.

Rise on to the toes of your standing foot as you rotate your kicking foot. Bouncing on it will give you a little extra height and time to move your other foot through a whole circle.

As you improve, you will learn how to cushion the ball as you catch it by withdrawing your foot ever-so-slightly when the ball makes contact. This will stop the ball pinging straight off again.

WITH CONFIDENCE, YOU WILL BE ABLE TO CONTINUE JUGGLING THE BALL, READY TO GO AGAIN WITH ANOTHER AROUND THE WORLD.

GO UNDERCOVER LIKE NOOR

NOOR INAYAT KHAN
Writer and spy

Lived: 1914-1944 in Russia, France, and England

Famous for: Being a super spy

Life changers: Joined the Women's Auxiliary Air Force (WAAF) in 1940 and was recruited as a special agent in 1942. She ran the Parisian spy network before being betrayed by a double agent.

YOU CAN DO IT!
Invent a secret identity

Noor was well educated and bilingual in French and English. She was a Special Operation Executive (SOE) agent, which involved being constantly on the move, in hiding, and changing her identity. Even when she was imprisoned and tortured, she refused to give away any secrets to her captors. Could you remember your cover story well enough to fool the enemy soldiers?

Give yourself a new name, address, and profession. Who will you be this time?

YOU CAN DO IT! Crack the secret code

Some messages are too sensitive to send in ordinary English or French. They have to be hidden in a code. This one, called pigpen, uses simple grids to assign a symbol to each letter.

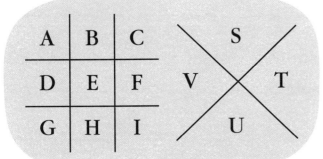

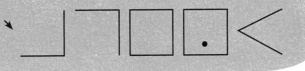

FOR EXAMPLE, "AGENT" WOULD BE WRITTEN LIKE THIS:

CAN YOU WRITE YOUR NAME USING THE CODE?

(Remember! You are working undercover. Which identity do you have this week?)

WHAT INSTRUCTIONS HAVE YOU RECEIVED HERE?

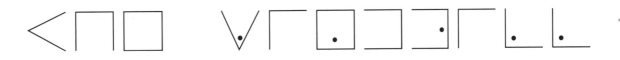

EXPRESS YOUR FEELINGS LIKE FRIDA

FRIDA KAHLO
Painter

Lived: 1907-1954 in Coyoacán, Mexico

Famous for: Paintings inspired by Mexican culture

Life changers: Having nearly died in a bus accident aged 18, her injuries prevented her from training as a doctor, so she began painting. She married the artist Diego Rivera who greatly influenced Frida's personal and professional life.

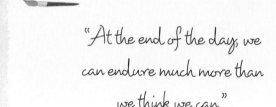

"At the end of the day, we can endure much more than we think we can."

Some of Kahlo's pain was physical—as well as the road accident, she suffered with polio as a child, forcing her to have surgery more than 30 times in her life. She was also badly hurt emotionally and endured many personal heartbreaks. She explored all of this in her work.

YOU CAN DO IT!
Paint from the heart

Frida Kahlo's paintings showed her Mexican influences, and also expressed her innermost feelings. She often produced self-portraits showing her passion, her vulnerability, and her pain. Kahlo often used animals to represent other things in her work. For her, monkeys were gentle and protective, while a black cat was bad luck.

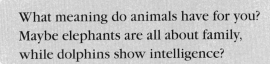

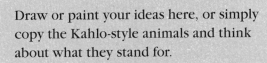

What meaning do animals have for you? Maybe elephants are all about family, while dolphins show intelligence?

Draw or paint your ideas here, or simply copy the Kahlo-style animals and think about what they stand for.

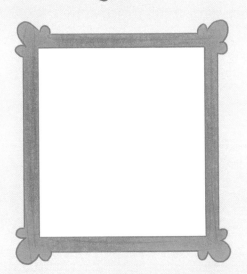

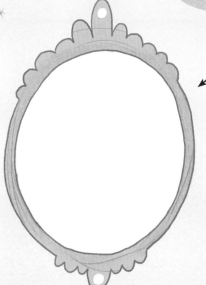

HOW ARE YOU FEELING TODAY?
WHAT SHAPES AND SHADES WOULD YOU USE TO SHOW IT?

DESIGN LIKE ZAHA

ZAHA HADID
Architect

Lived: 1950–2016 in Baghdad, Iraq, and London, UK

Famous for: Designing dramatic, curvy but practical buildings

Life changers: She studied at the Architectural Association (AA) which had a reputation for radical designs. In 1980, she started her own company, and then began to teach at top universities around the world.

"Yes, I am a feminist, because I see all women as smart, gifted, and tough."

Zaha Hadid designed inspirational, monumental, and unique buildings that shaped cities all around the world. She died only eight weeks after collecting the RIBA Royal Gold Medal. She was the first woman to receive the prize, which acknowledges a lifetime of great architecture.

YOU CAN DO IT!
Dream up your own building

Zaha's tutors encouraged her to produce daring, intelligent architecture. She refined her trademark style, creating curvy buildings such as the London Aquatics Centre for the 2012 Olympic Games, and the Heydar Alijev Center, an arts complex in Azerbaijan. She always considered not only the shapes, but the materials to be used.

What would you design? What would it be used for? What would it be made from?

FIGHT POLLUTION LIKE SYLVIA

SYLVIA EARLE
Marine biologist

Born: 1935 in USA

Famous for: Speaking out about pollution in the oceans

Life changers: After moving to the Gulf of Mexico aged 12, she fell in love with the ocean, and began diving and studying, completing two degrees in botany. She broke records with her exploratory deep-sea diving.

"Even if you never have the chance to see or touch the ocean, the ocean touches you with every breath you take, every drop of water you drink, every bite you consume."

Sylvia is bold, brave, and clever. She is hard-working, too! In 1979 she set a world record for an untethered (unattached) dive, descending 381 m (1,250 ft) to the seabed. She walked there for two hours, exploring depths that no diver had ever seen before.

YOU CAN DO IT!
Wage war on waste

Sylvia Earle has dedicated her life to marine exploration. She has served on national marine boards, led more than 50 expeditions, published more than 100 scientific papers, designed a submarine, and pushed the boundaries of deep-sea diving. Yet one of her most important role has been raising awareness about protecting the world's oceans. What can you do to help?

HOW YOU CAN HELP

- Say no to single-use plastic.

- Always take any wrappers or waste home to recycle.

- Carry your own reusable water bottle.

- Eat a piece of fruit instead of buying juice.

- "Take three for the sea"—remove three pieces of waste when you visit the beach.

- Join a group clean-up of a local park or beach or lake near you. These are often advertised on social media sites, so make sure you get your parents or carers involved.

- Use a bar of soap instead of liquid soap or shower gel.

- Fix things when they break instead of buying new ones.

- Make a compost pile for food waste.

YOU CAN DO IT!
Spread the word

Make a sign and display it in your car whenever you visit the coast. Cut pictures of sea creatures from magazines, and add warning signs with plastic bottles or other pollutants on them.

MAKE SURE IT HAS LOTS OF EXCLAMATION MARKS TO MAKE YOUR MESSAGE CLEAR!

DINO-DIG LIKE MARY

MARY ANNING
Paleontologist

Lived: 1799–1847 in Lyme Regis, UK

Famous for: Discovering the fossils of previously unknown creatures

Life changers: Mary's father died when Mary was only 11. The oldest of 10 children, she had to sell her fossil finds to support her family. Aged 12, she presented scientists with the first *Ichthyosaurus* bones ever discovered.

Mary Anning was no frail-hearted female. She often put herself in danger to find fossils. In 1833 she nearly died in a landslide that killed her dog, Tray.

"Mary Anning [was] probably the most important unsung (or inadequately sung) collecting force in the history of paleontology." Stephen Jay Gould

YOU CAN DO IT!
Uncover some real treats

Mary Anning had a special knack for finding prehistoric fossils, and for extracting and preparing them to sell to scientists and collectors. See if your skills match hers with this super dino-bones cake!

1. Begin with a cake. You can buy it or make it, and choose one you like best. Chocolate looks great but if you aren't a fan, pick vanilla sponge, coffee cake, or even coconut. It should be nice and firm.

2. Use fondant icing to make the bones. Roll small pieces into shape for the legs, backbones, and skull. Arrange them on top in a rough skeleton shape.

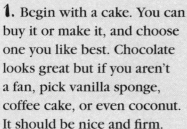

3. Now crunch up some dark brown cookies in a bag with a rolling pin. These are your soil. Sprinkle it all over the cake to cover up the bones. Spread chocolate spread around the sides of the cake, and stick some chocolate fingers or pretzel sticks to it, to make a fence.

4. Serve the cake with a clean paintbrush to uncover the bones, and a trowel-shaped cake cutter for an added paleontological flourish!

LEAVE A LEGACY LIKE ANNE

ANNE FRANK
Writer

Lived: 1929-1945 in Amsterdam, Netherlands

Famous for: Her diary written while hiding from the Nazi secret police

Life changers: Anne was only a small child when Hitler's policies against the Jews forced the Franks to leave Germany. She lived happily until World War II began. In 1942, her whole family was forced into hiding.

Anne's book has been translated into more than 70 languages and sold more than 30 million copies. It is one of the most powerful and moving pieces of wartime literature ever written.

"I still believe, in spite of everything, that people are really good at heart."

YOU CAN DO IT!
Keep a record of your life

Anne's days were spent in silence, hidden out of sight in a secret apartment concealed behind a bookcase. The family's friends brought them food, clothing, and books. Anne filled her days with studies, and keeping her diary. She wrote about her everyday life, composed short stories, and collected quotes. She also stuck photographs and letters into the diary.

MAKE A START BY WRITING ABOUT YOUR DAY HERE.

Add the date to this entry.

Describe the way you feel, as well as your everyday life.

Add comments about how other people reacted to things.

Write about things that happened today or this week.

Don't worry if you don't use complete sentences or correct spellings.

Stick in photos or do little drawings.

GET FIGHTING FIT LIKE MARY

MARY KOM
Boxer

Born: 1983 in Manipur, India

Famous for: First female Indian Olympic boxer

Life changers: Inspired by Muhammed Ali but not allowed to train, she learned to box in secret. She won the state boxing championship in 2000 without her father even knowing she had entered. She won Olympic Bronze in 2012 and Commonwealth Gold in 2018.

"Don't let anyone tell you you're weak because you're a woman."

YOU CAN DO IT!
Set up some circuit training

"Magnificent Mary" has had to overcome many obstacles to reach the top of her sport. Her family was so poor they sometimes went without food, and her father was very opinionated about the kinds of activities that weren't suitable for girls. Nowadays, Mary has used her experiences to help others, and has set up an academy to teach boxing to children from poor backgrounds. It's simple for you to train like a boxer without any special equipment.

Set up a circuit of small, individual exercises. Repeat each one ten times and then move on. You can repeat the whole circuit two or even three times, as your fitness improves.

Warm up

Jump rope or skipping is often part of a boxer's workout. It makes a great warm-up to get your heart pumping faster. Use a real rope if you have one, but if not, an imaginary rope works just fine. A two-minute warm-up will get your muscles ready.

Shadow boxing

Jab, cross, bob, and weave—now we're punching! Stand with one foot slightly in front of the other. Start with your elbows bent and fists guarding your face. Now jab—quickly punch one arm forward and rotate your fist down, then pull back.

Next, throw a cross with the opposite fist—punch forward, rotating your hip to allow your arm to move across your body. Raise your heel slightly off the floor. Pull back to the guard position.

Quickly duck down into a bob, with your knees and elbows bent and your fists held gently in front of your face. Practice moving lightly around from foot to foot on the spot as if ducking punches. Do this for 30 seconds, then rest for a few seconds.

DO FIVE QUICK REPETITIONS AND THEN SWAP TO THE OTHER FOOT AND DO FIVE REPS ON THE OTHER SIDE.

Bicycle crunches

Lie on your back with your legs outstretched. Bend your right leg to bring your knee up to your chest. At the same time pull your upper body into a crunch and try to touch your left elbow on your right knee.

Straighten out again and repeat with your right elbow and left knee. Do this ten times as fast as you can. Keep your chin tucked on to your chest to avoid straining your neck.

As you begin to feel fitter, add in more moves. Try push-ups, jumping jacks, sit-ups, or squat jumps.

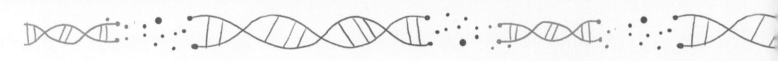

THINK LIKE MAY-BRITT

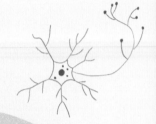

MAY-BRITT MOSER
Psychologist and neuroscientist

Born: 1963 in Fosnavåg, Norway

Famous for: Discovering the role of "grid cells" in the brain

Life changers: Studied in Oslo where she met and married Edvard Moser in 1985. Together they studied how the brain understands its surroundings and were awarded the Nobel Prize for their work.

May-Britt's work with her husband and their American–British mentor John O'Keefe has helped us to understand more about human memory and brain diseases such as Alzheimer's.

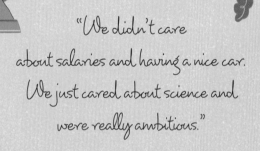

"We didn't care about salaries and having a nice car. We just cared about science and were really ambitious."

YOU CAN DO IT!
Make your brain and hands work together

The Mosers' Nobel Prize-winning work explored the way our brain cells represent space and position. See if you can spark up those cells and fold your own box from two pieces of paper.

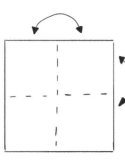

1. You will need two squares of paper, one slightly larger than the other. Take one piece and fold it in half. Unfold it and fold it in half the other way. Now you should have a cross in the middle.

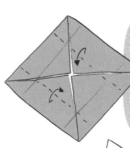

2. Fold each corner into the middle. Unfold and flip the paper over to the other side. Repeat, folding each corner into the middle on this side.

3. Unfold two of the points so it looks like this.

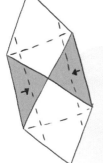

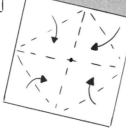

4. Now fold the lefthand side into the middle, the whole way along. This will make one side of the box base. Do the same with the righthand side.

5. With the box sides standing upright, fold down one pointed end, pushing in the two triangles that appear from your original creases.

6. You should now be able to fold down the pointed end so it sits in the base of the box, and the third box side is formed.

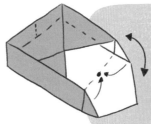

7. Repeat at the opposite end, running your fingers along the creases to make everything stay nicely in place.

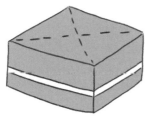

8. DO EXACTLY THE SAME WITH THE OTHER PIECE, AND YOU WILL GET A BASE AND A LID THAT FIT BEAUTIFULLY TOGETHER.

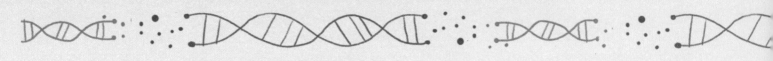

LIGHT UP LIKE MÁRIA

MÁRIA TELKES
Scientist and inventor

Lived: 1900-1995 in Budapest, Hungary and the US

Famous for: Pioneering inventions using solar power

Life changers: Moved to the US in 1924 to work as a biochemist, and began to study how to use solar energy in the late 1930s. She created several breakthrough solar technologies from stoves to systems for heating houses.

She was a prolific inventor of thermal devices, and was given the nickname "the Sun Queen."

Mária worked with architect Eleanor Raymond after World War II to create the first house that was heated by solar energy. In 1952 she received the first Society of Women Engineers Achievement Award.

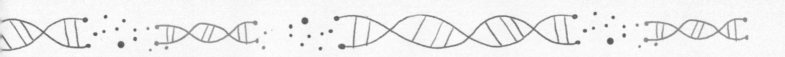

YOU CAN DO IT!
Turn salty water into drinking water

One of Mária Telkes's most important inventions was a solar-powered contraption that could turn seawater into fresh water. She invented it in World War II and likely saved the lives of airmen and sailors who were abandoned at sea and would have died without drinking water. Give it a try for yourself!

1. Make your own salt water. Add two spoons of table salt to a large bowl of warm water. Stir it until the salt dissolves, and let it cool.

2. Place an empty glass into the bowl, the right way up. Ensure the top is sticking up above the saltwater and is completely clean and empty. You may need to place a weight in the bottom to keep it still.

3. Cover the bowl with plastic wrap. It should form a tight seal around the large bowl, but not touch the rim of the glass. Add a pebble or coin on top to weigh it down in the middle.

4. Place it in bright sunlight for several hours. As the water heats up, it will rise and form condensation beneath the plastic wrap. This will be fresh water, as the salt does not evaporate. It should trickle to the middle where the weight is and collect in the glass below. The water that drips into the glass will be safe to drink.

BE A RAPTIVIST LIKE SONITA

SONITA ALIZADEH
Rap artist and activist

Born: 1997 in Afghanistan but escaped to Iran

Famous for: Going viral with her rap song "Brides for Sale"

Life changers: Caught on camera aged 16 being told that her mother had found a husband to buy her; expressed how she felt in a rap song; moved to the US to avoid the marriage.

Sonita's rap inspirations include Eminem and the Iranian rapper Yas. Whose music inspires you?

"To the women of my beloved country: believe in yourselves. You are strong. Speak up about your dreams and your goals every day so that everyone knows that you exist."

YOU CAN DO IT! Flex your rhymes

Although the sale of young women as brides is common in Afghanistan, Sonita was shocked that it was going to happen to her. She wrote about her fear and despair in a rap song and uploaded it to YouTube. Many rappers write about topics that are close to their heart. It gives their lyrics and performances more heartfelt meaning. Give it a go! Make some notes here and see where it takes you.

MAKE MUSIC LIKE ZHANG

XIAN ZHANG
Conductor

Born: 1973 in Dandong, Liaoning province, China

Famous for: Conducting orchestras in a male-dominated profession

Life changers: Left home at 13 to study music in Beijing, and led an orchestra for the first time aged 19. She moved to the US in 1998 where she joined the New York Philharmonic Orchestra.

Xian's mother trained as a pianist and started to coach Xian when she was three years old. Later, Xian's teacher at music school said her hands were too small to be a concert pianist, so she decided to be a conductor instead.

"I was lucky in that what my parents wanted me to do and trained me for was what I wanted to do."

YOU CAN DO IT!
Spot the difference

From the moment she was born, Xian Zhang was surrounded by music. Her father worked in a factory that made violins and guitars, and later owned a music shop. Her mother taught piano. Look very carefully to find ten differences between these two musical scenes of Xian in action.

DO YOU KNOW?

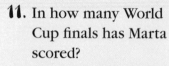

1. Which Vostok mission did Valentina Tereshkova undertake?

2. Why was Xian Zhang told she couldn't be a concert pianist?

3. Which of the Williams sisters is the oldest?

4. What was the name of Sonita Alizadeh's rap song that first brought her wide attention?

5. What covered the entrance to Anne Frank's secret hiding place?

6. How old was Malala Yousafzai when she received the Nobel Peace Prize?

7. What were Kenyan women paid to do by Wangari Maathai's Green Belt Movement?

8. What name is given to a protest where a person refuses to eat?

9. When was J.K. Rowling's first book in the Harry Potter series published?

10. Which prehistoric creature's bones did Mary Anning uncover when she was 12?

11. In how many World Cup finals has Marta scored?

12. What is the name of Sylvia Earle's mini research submarine, invented in 1982?

13. Noor Inayat Khan joined the WAAF and was an SOE. What do the initials stand for?

14. For which Olympic Games did Zaha Hadid design a curvy Aquatics Centre?

15. In which part of the body are the grid cells studied by May-Britt Moser?

16. What was Frida Kahlo's professional ambition as a child?

1. Vostok 6 2. Her hands were too small 3. Venus 4. Brides for Sale 5. A bookcase 6. 17 7. Plant trees 8. Hunger strike 9. 1997 10. Ichthyosaurus 11. 5 12. Deep Rover 13. Women's Auxiliary Air Force and Special Operation Executive 14. London 2012 15. The brain 16. To be a doctor

ASK ME ANYTHING!

Speak to your mother, stepmother, aunt, grandmother, carer, or teacher to discover their stories and their own experiences. Here are some questions to get you started:

WHO WERE YOUR FEMALE HEROES GROWING UP?

WHAT ARE THE MOST IMPORTANT LESSONS THAT YOU HAVE LEARNT?

WHAT WOULD YOU LIKE TO SEE WOMEN ACHIEVE IN THE FUTURE?

WHAT ACHIEVEMENT ARE YOU MOST PROUD OF?

HAVE YOU OVERCOME DIFFICULTIES TO ACHIEVE YOUR GOALS?

WHICH WOMEN DO YOU ADMIRE TODAY?

AS A CHILD, WHAT DID YOU WANT TO BE WHEN YOU GREW UP?

WHAT ADVICE WOULD YOU GIVE YOUNG WOMEN TODAY?

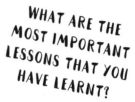

Remember that some people might not want to answer one or more of your questions. If that's the case, be respectful and move on to the next question, or simply ask someone else who is keen to share their story. If you want to record their answers, you must ask for permission first.

INDEX